Karen

THOSE MAGNIFICENT CLYDESDALES

THE GENTLE GIANTS

THOSE MAGNIFICENT

BROOKE HOUSE

Los Angeles, California

CLYDESDALES

~ THE GENTLE GIANTS ~

KAREN C. FLANIGAN

Library of Congress Cataloging in Publication Data

Flanigan, Karen C.
    Those magnificent Clydesdales.

    1. Clydesdale horse.   I. Title.
SF293.C65F56   636.1'5   76-56101
ISBN 0-912588-02-0

7890123987654321

Distributed in Canada by Van Nostrand Reinhold, Ltd.

Photography Credits

Anheuser-Busch, Inc.: i, 1, 11, 15, 18, 22, 25, 27, 31, 33, 35,
                43, 46, 48, 49, 51, 52, 53, 54,
                front jacket, front case
Kevin F. Burke: back jacket, back case
Herbert Bruce Cross: 19
D'Arcy-MacManus & Masius, Inc.: 4, 9, 16, 21, 24, 41, 56
Chuck Dresner: 8
Jack Fahland: 34
Berry Farrell: 5
Fleishman-Hillard, Inc.: 32, 36, 37, 44, 45
Michael M. Gill: 40
Kristen Peterson: 13, 28, 29
John Santos: 42
Edwin D. Schneckloth: 7

Design by Barbara Monahan

To my grandfather, August A. Busch, Jr.
—through his wisdom, the Clydesdale breed prospers
in the United States and delights the hearts of many.

CONTENTS

ACKNOWLEDGMENTS

Special thanks to my mother and best friend, who supported my every need!

My heartfelt thanks to Louis Eaton, Barbara Monahan, and Kevin Burke, who made my book possible.

My deep appreciation to those who were of assistance: Anheuser-Busch, Inc., Harlan Conley, Berry Farrell, Fleishman-Hillard, Inc., D'Arcy-MacManus & Masius, "Whitey" Mueller, Bob Garrick, Santos Leather Shop, Kristen Peterson, Billy Anders, Clydesdale Horse Society of Great Britain & Ireland, and the Clydesdale Breeders Association of the United States.

Thanks for their encouragement to family, friends, and especially Brad Reynolds.

THOSE MAGNIFICENT CLYDESDALES

≈ THE GENTLE GIANTS ≈

Think when we talk of horses that you see them
Printing their proud hoofs i' th' receiving earth.

SHAKESPEARE
Henry V

As a little girl growing up in St. Louis, one of my earliest memories is the tingling excitement of the Clydesdales on parade—the sound of thirty-two thundering hooves pounding the pavement and the spectacle of the magnificent bay horses, with muscles rippling, ears alert, and silky feathered legs rotating like one giant machine. Their fiery red wagon gleamed in the sun, and the driver, dalmatian by his side, held sixty-seven pounds of leather reins to manage the eight tons of horsepower. The majestic horses, known and loved as the "gentle giants," captured my heart then, as they continue to capture the hearts of thousands today. This is their story.

CHAPTER 1

HISTORY

Specific ancestry of the Clydesdales is uncertain, but it is thought the breed descended from equus robustus, a primitive horse of the Pleistocene Epoch, one million years ago. This strain evolved in the fertile plains of Western Europe, and with plentiful and nutritious food, and temperate climate, equus robustus grew into a massive and powerful beast. Because of his size and strength, few animals dared to challenge him, so survival of the species was assured.

Descendants of this large horse were first observed in the years of the Roman Empire. During his campaigns in Gaul, Julius Caesar noted the Gallic army using large heavy horses for transporting supplies. He was quick to perceive the military importance of such a horse and had several sent to Rome for interbreeding.

History of large horses is sparse between Roman times and the Middle Ages, but they do appear occasionally in Western European paintings and tapestries, most notably in battle scenes. Kings and chieftains often rode "high horses," as they were called, to indicate their stature and so all the soldiers could easily see their leader. The current expression "get off your high horse" may be derived from this custom. By 1100 A.D., the celebrated "great horse" of medieval times was quite common in France, the Lowlands, and England. This was the sturdy, powerful mount that carried King Richard the Lionheart and the Crusaders to the Holy Land. In the colorful tales and legends of the age of chivalry, great horses shared the exploits of Ivanhoe and King Arthur, Sir Lancelot, and the knights of the Round Table; even Sir Galahad probably rode one in search of the Holy Grail.

During the Middle Ages, the great horse

4

was bred for more speed and coordination as he was required to carry knights into battle and in jousting tournaments. Considering that a knight with armor, shield, and trappings weighed close to three hundred pounds, we know that the horse must indeed have been "great" in size, strength, and mobility.

With the waning of the Middle Ages, knights on horseback passed into history, and descendants of the great horse were used more for farming and heavy labor. The importance of these animals for domestic work was reflected in the extensive horse trading that began in Europe in the early 1400s. As European civilization began to flourish, every country needed strong, sturdy horses, and champion stallions and mares were highly prized acquisitions.

Scotland was no exception. The rough, hilly farmland of this country especially required large, strong horses, and it was here in the county of Lanarkshire that the ancestors of the gentle giants were born. Lanarkshire is a colorful county

Left, *Clydesdale mare and foal in meadow*
Right, *Clydesdales grazing*

in southeast Scotland where skirling bagpipes echo over the heather meadows and dales. The river Clyde waters a fertile valley in the central county near the town of Lanark, popularly known as Clydesdale. In the early eighteenth century, the local farmers began importing prize Flemish and Dutch stallions to service their native breeds, hoping to increase the size and strength of their horses. These descendants of the medieval great horse reproduced, consistently handing down fine characteristics to their colts and fillies and providing a basis for a hardy breed of draft horse.

Blaze, a famous black stallion born in 1779, had important influence in determining the Clydesdale individuality. Blaze was foaled with a wide, white stripe covering the middle of his face and four snow-white, kneelength stockings. The majority of Blaze's descendants received his white markings on both face and legs, but generally his black coloring is not typical today. By the 1830s, Lanarkshire and bordering counties exchanged studs to introduce new blood lines. As before, this was done to increase the size and strength of the strain. Once perfected, these draft horses became known as the famous Clydesdale breed, honoring the name of the valley from which they came. The system of exchanging studs continues today and is beneficial in distributing superior sires to maintain the quality of the Clydesdale breed.

In the 1870s, three organizations were formed to promote the Clydesdales. Begun in about 1870, the world-renowned annual Glasgow Stallion Show is still an impressive display of hundreds of draft horses. It is a spectacle to see the scores of spotlessly groomed stallions standing proudly in the judging ring. The winning stallion is always an unforgettable champion and is heavily sought after to service mares. The Clydesdale Breed Society, founded in Scotland in 1878, and the Clydesdale Breeders Association, established in the United States in 1879, also actively continue today.

By the year 1879, the Clydesdales were recognized as a distinct breed. By that time, breeders had begun exporting these horses abroad. The first Clydesdales brought into North America were probably imported into Canada by Scottish residents. By the 1880s, many Clydesdales were being used in the United States.

Horses had always been essential to the early settlers of America for both travel and work. They were needed to carry heavy materials and to pull wagons, plows, and other loads. Then in the late eighteen and early nineteen hundreds, further specialization of machinery required horses with the size, endurance, and temperament suitable for pulling cumbersome loads and farm equipment. These bigger horses also had to pull heavy carts without siding called drays, which handled all freight on the streets of the cities and towns. Since Clydesdales can pull loads up to two tons, they were ideally suited for such work and became very popular and useful on farms and in cities.

Many trades were created around the powerful horses. Every community had a blacksmith shop and a harness shop; other businesses

Trophy for Clydesdale competition

7

produced horseshoes, saddles, buggies, wagons, and countless farming equipment to be drawn by horses.

Today, however, horses are not vital to farming and industry. Work horses lost their popularity and demand when scientific progress replaced them with tractors, combine harvesters, automobiles, trucks, and other sophisticated machinery.

But even though the daily responsibilities of work horses were eliminated and their future endangered, the love for and dedication to the Clydesdales has never wavered. Today they are still effective in deep mud and on steep hills where tractors find it impossible to maneuver or climb. Fairs are reopening their draft horse classes and attracting more and more participation and enthusiasm. Parades, exhibitions, and horse shows have found that the Clydesdales are a magnetic crowd attraction. The gentle giants are exciting and unforgettable—once you see them, you are drawn back whenever they return to town.

Left, *Clydesdale foal with mare in background*
Right, *Harnessed Clydesdales heather-stepping through gate*

and by this standard, a Clydesdale normally measures 5 feet 11 inches to his withers.

The weight of a Clydesdale is an extraordinary 1 ton or 2,000 pounds. It is even possible for a mature stallion or gelding in prime condition to weigh up to 2,300 pounds.

DIMENSIONS

Horses are one of Earth's oldest mammals. They began their parade of evolution some fifty million years ago as equines, before the human race existed. Originally, these horses were only the size of a pet dog or a large cat. It is hard to believe that an animal so small could grow and change into a majestic Clydesdale.

Although the Clydesdales are slightly smaller than other draft horses, such as the Belgians and Percherons, they are still enormous. The average height of a Clydesdale is approximately 17 to 18½ hands, 1 hand equalling 4 inches. A horse is measured from the ground to his withers, which is directly over his front shoulder;

	height	*weight*
Lilliputian	24 to 26 inches	200 to 250 pounds
Mule	36 to 40 inches	560 to 600 pounds
Clydesdale	68 to 74 inches	2,000 to 2,300 pounds

Size comparison of Lilliputian, Mule, and Clydesdale

CHAPTER 3

CARE AND GROOMING

Extensive care is necessary to keep a Clydesdale in prime condition. Let us take a typical day in the life of a pampered, loved, and well-groomed Anheuser-Busch Clydesdale show horse. The "alarm clock" for the Clydesdale rings early with the first hint of sunlight, the roosters crowing, and an arousing good-morning pat on the rump from a stableman. If the night has been cold or damp, the stableman removes the warm, cozy blanket that covers the massive body. After fetching a fresh bucket of water, he serves the horse a hearty, hot meal. This repast, scrumptious to the horse, is a mixture of oats, grain, dried beet pulp, molasses, salt, and hot water. Sometimes the chef adds a few extra vitamins to the thirty quarts of grain consumed by the Clydesdale each day. After breakfast, a fifty-pound bale of timothy hay is set in the hay bin for the horse to snack on when he is hungry during the day. Also, because horses need a large quantity of salt daily, a salt lick is always in the stall.

Keeping a Clydesdale well fed and at the proper weight is the best way to prove affection for him. Nothing is more valuable to the health of a horse than what he eats. No matter how large the horse, his stomach is small in proportion to his size. It is advisable to leave hay in the stall to give him the opportunity to eat when he feels like it, but the regular feed should be given at set intervals. Breakfast is served between 6:30 and 7:00 in the morning, and dinner is served around 6:00 at night. Like a person, if a Clydesdale does not eat on time, his stomach loudly rumbles.

Because horses have a slow digestive system, after the Clydesdale has finished his breakfast,

Clydesdale at feeding bin with duck

a stableman brings him to the paddocks or a grassy pasture to stretch, graze, and run with other Clydesdales. Once in the pasture, most will run freely, but some must be lunged with a lead line to get enough exercise. While the Clydesdales are out in the field, the stablemen clean up their stalls and place a fresh bed of clean straw in each.

Following their workout, the horses return to the washroom for grooming. Keeping a Clydesdale well manicured not only maintains his beauty, but also helps clean his skin and keep it free from chapping. Proper grooming reduces the chance of disease and parasites and also improves muscle condition. Many horses enjoy the bathing and the soft strokes of the currycomb and brushes and stand with head drooping and eyes lazily closed, enjoying every minute of relaxation and "tender loving care." Still, it is best to groom as quickly as possible to guard against the horse reacting nervously and to avoid irritating his skin.

Various materials are needed to groom a Clydesdale: a hoof pick to remove all debris caught between the horse's frog and horseshoe; a rubber or metal currycomb to loosen the dirt and scurf in the hair; a dandy brush to remove the light dirt and dust from the skin; a body brush to clean the body; a mane and tail comb to untangle any knotted areas; a sweat scraper to remove any excess water; a grooming cloth eighteen to twenty-four inches square to rub and polish the coat; and a specialized horse vacuum cleaner to fluff up the coat and remove any dirt, dust, and dandruff.

With all this equipment, it seems that the grooming of a Clydesdale would take hours of hard labor, but an experienced Anheuser-Busch stableman can do it in twenty to thirty minutes.

The legs and feet are an invaluable part of any horse. If something goes wrong with either, he could become lame and unable to walk and perform. The ailment might be temporary, but there is always the possibility of permanent damage. So whenever the stableman cleans the hoof, he must

Anatomy of famous Anheuser-Busch Clydesdale named Peanuts

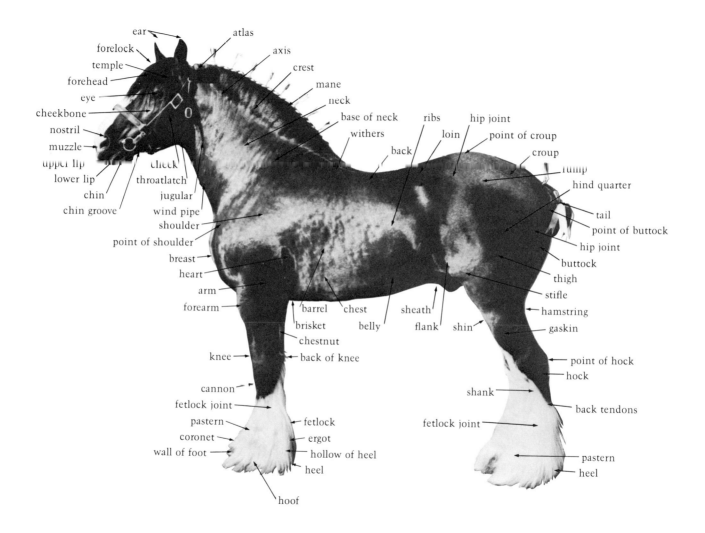

ear
forelock
temple
forehead
eye
cheekbone
nostril
muzzle
upper lip
lower lip
chin
chin groove
cheek
throatlatch
jugular
wind pipe
shoulder
point of shoulder
breast
heart
arm
forearm
barrel
brisket
chestnut
chest
belly
sheath
flank
shin
knee
back of knee
cannon
fetlock joint
pastern
coronet
wall of foot
fetlock
ergot
hollow of heel
heel
hoof
atlas
axis
crest
mane
neck
base of neck
withers
back
ribs
loin
point of croup
croup
rump
hip joint
hind quarter
tail
point of buttock
hip joint
buttock
thigh
stifle
hamstring
gaskin
point of hock
hock
shank
back tendons
fetlock joint
pastern
heel

check to see that the shoe is securely fastened and that no nails are missing or misplaced. In order to pick up the foot, he slides his hand down the leg until he reaches the fetlock, straddling the horse's leg with his own legs. In his left hand, he holds the hoof while, with his other hand, he holds the pick to clean the hoof. Once the hoof is comfortably placed, the stableman cleans its depressions.

Currycombing the body is like giving the horse a massage. With the comb in his right hand and the brush in his left, the stableman proceeds from the left side, stroking the neck, breast, withers, shoulders, foreleg down to the knee, backside, belly, croup, and hindleg down to the hock. During this process, he frequently removes the hair and dust from the comb and brush. Currycombing is accomplished simply through small, circular, gentle strokes.

Brushing requires stronger, rougher movements. The stableman brushes the hair in the direction that it grows. He uses the most common grooming tool, the body brush, for the head, body, mane, and tail. Then he smooths the mane and tail with downward motions of the mane and tail comb.

Once or twice a month, the stableman washes the mane and tail in lukewarm water, using a bar of mild castile soap, a popular cleansing agent that eliminates any gummy film on the horse's coat. He *never* washes the gigantic body with soap because it dries out the skin severely and removes important oils that keep the coat shiny and healthy. Each day the stableman splashes and rubs down the horse with a warm-water hose to rinse him off and refresh him. Special oils rubbed into the coat replace any oils that might have been lost during grooming.

If necessary, the stableman tidies up the eyes, ears, face, lips, and nostrils with the grooming cloth.

Clipping and shearing are performed only when necessary. The stableman trims the hair

Clydesdales crossing stream

18

from the inside of the ears, around the jaw, and under the neck. He never clips the feathers—the silky, fine hairs that fall below the knees and hocks and cover the ankles and hooves. Since these long, delicate feathers touch the ground, they are sheared naturally in the horse's normal activity.

These feathers are unique to Clydesdale and Shire draft horses. Although they do not require cutting, they do need to be rinsed daily to be kept spotlessly clean. At least once a week, the stableman again uses the natural castile soap, but this time he adds granulated sulfur to enhance the soft, white coloring of the feathers. Each feathered foot requires a good twenty to thirty minutes of this special attention with soap. After rinsing each leg, the stableman generously coats the feathers with lathering soap and massages and washes them. Then he hoses off the remaining bubbles and dries the feathered feet by rubbing scented, clean sawdust up and down each leg by hand for ten minutes.

Blacksmith shoeing a Clydesdale

The artful grooming of a Clydesdale brings out his finest qualities. With his feathers snowy white, his mane and tail clean, and his body rinsed, the gentle giant stands tall and walks with pride—as if to show off his elegance to admirers.

The value of any horse is essentially his ability to move, so it is imperative to keep both his feet and legs in superior condition. A concerned and responsible blacksmith or stableman always checks each horse's feet to see that they are clean, to prevent any drying out, and to keep the hooves trimmed at their proper length, shape, and fit.

The specially trained blacksmith shoes each Clydesdale every four to six weeks. Every Clydesdale shoe is handcrafted. The blacksmith, standing in front of a blazing forge with a twenty- to twenty-two-inch straight bar of steel in his hand, transforms the metal into a Clydesdale horseshoe by carefully molding and sculpturing it. This process of heating the steel and bending it into a form-fitting shape is a talent few possess

Comparison of Mule, Thoroughbred, and Clydesdale horseshoes

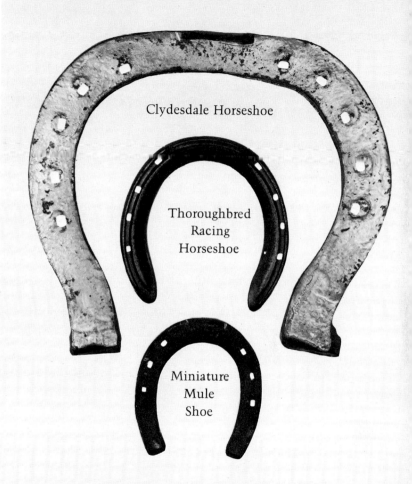

Clydesdale Horseshoe

Thoroughbred Racing Horseshoe

Miniature Mule Shoe

(37 percent actual size)

19

today. It takes an hour to make only one shoe. Each handmade horseshoe is attached to the hoof by eight number twelve nails each three inches long. Once the shoe is made, it weighs 3¾ pounds and is twice the size and four times the weight of an ordinary horseshoe.

To prepare an Anheuser-Busch Clydesdale for showing, the stableman must also braid the tail and roll the mane. Braiding the tail makes the horse's hips look larger and keeps his tail from swishing out over the reins of the other horses in the hitch. Rolling the mane accentuates the horse's beauty.

To braid the tail, the stableman first combs and brushes the tail until there are no tangles. He then carefully divides the hair into three strands, leaving the heaviest strand in the middle and braiding as tightly as possible. After a few twists down the tail, he twines the ribbon into the braid, knotting the ribbon at the end of the tail to look like a necktie. At this point, he slips a heavy looped wire through the hair, catching the bottom of the tail and bringing it up to attach at the top of the tail. Two strands of string wrapped tightly around this hair ball secure the knot. On top of this, the stableman ties a ribbon in a bow tie around the ball of tail to give it the final decorative touch.

It takes agile hands with strong fingers to roll the mane by braiding the separate tufts of hair with their ribbon bunting. The stableman ties two 40-inch lengths of bunting together with a knot at the top of the mane and braids and twists together two strands of hair about ¾ inch long with the bunting. He continues this procedure down the crest of the neck to the front of the shoulder, braiding as tightly as possible to keep the bunting and hair in place. He ties the ends of the bunting in a slip knot over the lumped braid to complete the show preparations for the hitch horse.

Handsomely groomed champion Clydesdale

BREEDING

There are many different systems of breeding, and the breeder chooses a system depending on the size and quality of his herd, the money available, the skill of the stableman, and the desired goals for the breed. The Anheuser-Busch Clydesdales utilize the linebreeding method of reproduction, which involves servicing half brothers to sisters, cousins to cousins, or descendants to grandsires to keep the offspring as closely related as possible to family lines and inherited traits. Genes determine the Clydesdale heredity. Through this linebreeding, the Anheuser-Busch Clydesdales all have the characteristic feathered feet, similar coloring, and desirable markings, conformation, and disposition.

Breeding two Clydesdales can be difficult

Anheuser-Busch breeding farm

and requires expert supervision. Of all the mares bred each year, only about half conceive, and even then, some mares conceive but give birth to unhealthy foals who cannot survive or foals who are dead at birth. Therefore, it is advantageous to service two mares in order to ensure one strong, healthy, superior foal.

In selecting a stallion, it is in the breeder's interest to pick a purebred Clydesdale with desirable attributes. The stallion should be at least three to four years old. For horses, one year is the equivalent of seven human years; so by our measurement, the stallion is twenty-one to twenty-eight years of age at this point and fully mature in size and bone structure.

To safeguard his health, the stallion should service a mare only twice a day, preferably once early in the morning and again in the late afternoon. It is advisable to allow the stallion to rest a full day once a week. He should also be allowed to exercise in a large, lush pasture, where he can freely forage and roam.

The broodmares chosen for servicing must be two to three years old and distinguished for their disposition, conformation, size, and coloring. The mares come into season every twenty-one days and are capable of conceiving for seven days. Sometimes it is difficult to detect when the mares are in season as the Clydesdales bleed very little externally, but knowledgable stablemen can spot the time. The mare is more responsive to the stallion and seems to desire more companionship.

While in season, a mare is serviced as many as three or four times to insure impregnation. After three weeks, blood or urine tests easily determine if the mare is in foal. The mating process of a Clydesdale mare and stallion is a rather swift and unemotional experience. The courtship may include some rubbing and biting gestures on the part of the stallion, but the mating relationship between the two horses involves only simple instinct for reproduction.

Left, *Clydesdales running freely in pasture*
Right, *Herd of Clydesdales at Anheuser-Busch breeding farm*

24

CHAPTER 5

FOALING

Once the mare is pregnant, she seems to glow with a sense of pride and fulfillment. Her trim body fills out quickly, gaining 150 to 200 pounds in the eleven months she carries the foal. Her belly grows and expands until she appears ready to burst.

While in foal, the mare's feeding and exercising habits should be carefully monitored. She must receive the proper vitamins and nutrients and must exercise regularly to keep herself in condition and the foal healthy and strong inside her.

As the foaling time approaches, the mare's buttocks muscles near the tail begin to thin down and her abdomen drops. Four to six days before the foaling, her teats enlarge. She shows signs of nervousness and restlessness by changing her position constantly.

Foaling can take place either in a grassy pasture or within the four walls of a cozy, clean stall. Because breeders feel extreme weather does not treat the mother and foal with kindness, generally the foaling does take place in a stall.

The newborn 110- to 125-pound Clydesdale drops from the mare into the hay cushioning of his new home. The mare and foal are usually still connected by the umbilical cord. After a short time, due to pulling and stretching, the cord breaks itself in two near the mare and the veterinarian or stableman treats the wound with a tincture of iodine or another popular antiseptic. The mare washes off the furry, damp, little body with her tongue; and then the stableman rubs the foal with a towel.

She then closely inspects the ears, which lie

Right, *Tiny Clydesdale foal*
Following pages: left, *One-hour-old Clydesdale foal;* center, *Foal and mare nuzzling;* right, *Foal nursing from mare*

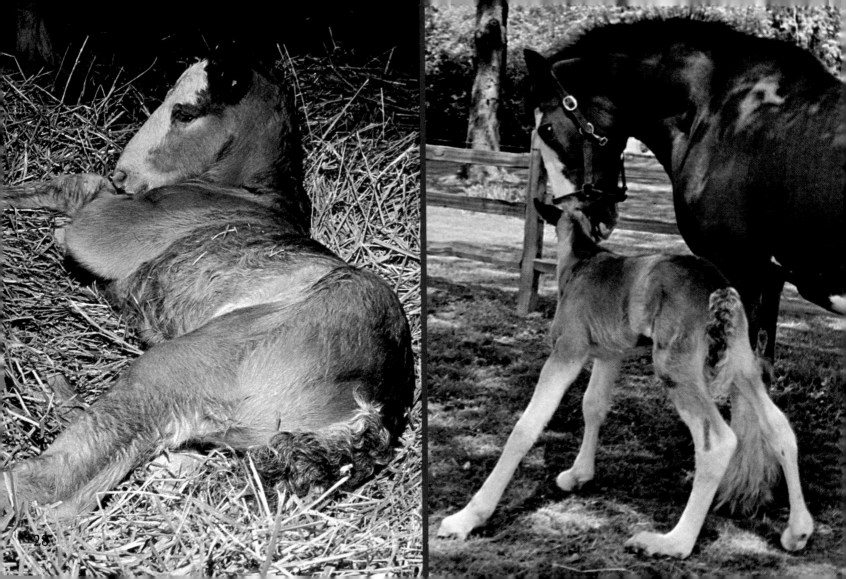

flat on the foal's head for protection during foaling, and the tall, skinny, featherless legs and hooves, checking to see that her little one is healthy and comfortable. At birth, the four petite hooves are soft and extremely tender. This is nature's way of protecting the mother while the foal is in her womb. After being exposed to the air, it takes the hooves only a few days to become stiff and hard. The adorable face with the wide blaze; the long, thick, half- to one-inch eyelashes; and the huggable body make the foal irresistible. It is amazing to watch the mare's careful footing around the foal—she is so gentle and sensitive to his needs.

The little Clydesdale foal is usually energetic, eager to try out his new legs and curious to investigate his mother. After thirty to sixty minutes, the foal attempts to lift himself up. With great frustration and no luck, he finds himself toppling over, back into the soft hay. His wobbly legs are just not strong enough to carry his body until two or three hours after birth.

When the foal finally gains a wobbly footing, he begins nursing from his mother. During the first few days of nursing, the mare's milk is highly concentrated in protein and vitamins to protect the foal from contagious infections that might harm him. The foal is usually hungry every fifteen to thirty minutes; then he nuzzles close to his mother, drinking until satisfied.

CHAPTER 6

DISPOSITION

The exceptionally quiet disposition of the Clydesdales is remarkable; even people close to them are amazed that such giants can be so gentle. The horses are never nervous and rarely do they kick or bolt. They are particularly relaxed and patient with people; and although precautions are always taken to insure the safety of admirers, it would be highly unlikely for a Clydesdale to hurt anyone intentionally. Nature's protective methods cause the Clydesdales to see objects and people twice their natural size. This enables man to control the horses more effectively because the horses do not realize they are as overpowering as they are.

Clydesdales are highly regarded for their majestic presence and bearing. Their flamboyance, vitality, and high-stepping gait make them unique among draft horses. Performing in parades, in show rings, and at rodeos always displays their incomparable spirit! They step out proudly, lifting their legs gracefully in the characteristic heather step and carrying their heads high. Despite their size and weight, they carry themselves with ease and agility.

A gentle giant

CHAPTER 7

CHARACTERISTICS

A Clydesdale horse with perfect conformation would be bay or brown in color with a wide white blaze down the center of his face. Occasionally a foal will be born black, roan, or chestnut with minimal white markings, but careful breeding tries to insure uniform coloring.

The Clydesdale's head has a broad expanse across the eyes; the nostrils are large; the eyes are intelligent and sparkling clear; a well-arched, elongated neck protrudes from an oblique shoulder; the back is short and strong; the legs bulge with solid, resilient muscle; the rear legs stand with their hocks facing toward one another; and the feathers, that keep water from infecting the feet, are abundant, long, and spotlessly white; the feet are open and massive with round hooves. The feet are very important in a Clydesdale; to carry his weight, his feet and limbs must be exceptionally durable.

Left, *Clydesdale mare and foal with preferred conformation*
Right, *Clydesdale grazing*

33

Exercising a Clydesdale

ANHEUSER-BUSCH HITCH TRAINING

For the first two years of his life, the Anheuser-Busch Clydesdale has freedom to run, play in the sun, doze, and find playmates among the other foals. During this time, experts constantly watch the foal to determine his future.

When the foal is two years old, his life changes abruptly. Anheuser-Busch might sell him (or her), keep him (or her) for breeding, or begin to train and school him to possibly become part of the impressive eight-horse hitch.

Training is given in distinct stages to accustom the colt gradually to his new routine. He now has a stall of his own; and he learns to appreciate, or at least endure, the necessary grooming attentions. The stableman brushes and currycombs him and painlessly trims his four feet. Only his two front hooves receive light shoes; his back feet remain unshod for a while longer.

After he has adjusted to his new living quarters and the pampering, he receives his first harness and bit. Some of the colts adapt quickly and react with pride; others take some time before they feel comfortable and relaxed in their new trimmings.

Once the colt is at ease with the harness and bit, the trainer hitches him to a wagon next to a casual "old timer." Accustomed to bewildered students, the older horse acts both as a coach and an anchor in case his young partner decides to bolt. Although the colt is not yet fully grown, his tremendous power would be too strong for one man to restrain. At this time, the trainer takes out of training a few horses of exceptional conformation and disposition and keeps them solely as studs.

Harnessing a Clydesdale for the hitch

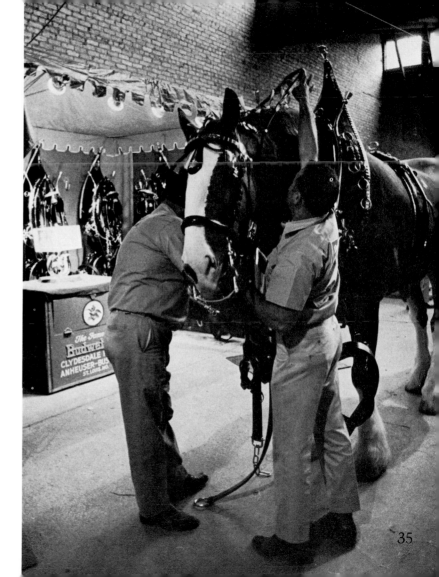

The requirements for becoming part of the hitch are rigid. A hitch horse must be a gelded male; stand eighteen hands high; be bay in color; have four white, full, feathered feet, a white blaze down the middle of his face, and a black mane and tail. The final requirement is crucial: he must be calm. While on tour, it is essential the Clydesdale hitch horse be even tempered in order to adjust to any situation.

Years of learning and practice enable the huge eight-horse hitch to handle the wagon effortlessly. At horse shows, rodeos, and annual openings of Santa Anita in Arcadia, California, the horses pull the 3½-ton, shining red, antique Budweiser beer wagon in a series of intricate maneuvers that were their ancestors' when they were delivering beer and produce to stores and bars. They perform this spectacular display of precision and coordination for the public's entertainment year round.

Left, *Thrilled children with Clydesdales*
Right, *Head of harnessed Clydesdale*

37

CHAPTER 9

ANHEUSER-BUSCH HITCH

"Slower. Faster. Back up. Circle." When performing in an exhibition, each Clydesdale responds quickly to the driver's slightest command. To assure the control the driver needs in his hands and voice, every horse in the hitch is trained by name. Eight separate reins, together weighing sixty-seven pounds, lace through the driver's hands while he drives the eight tons of horse-power. Because each horse has individual reins, many times the driver's hands cross over to manipulate a particular Clydesdale.

The Anheuser-Busch Clydesdale performance usually consists of various traditional maneuvers. First, the eight horses skillfully swing in circles to create a series of figure eights. The second maneuver exhibits the control and response of the horses in smoothly backing up to place the wagon close to the street curb. Years ago they did this to unload the wagon's beer at the loading docks. The wagon and horses had to hug the curb calmly in order not to disturb other horses and wagons in passing traffic.

In the third maneuver, the horses pull away from the curb back into the line of traffic. The first pair, which are furthest from the wagon, are the lead horses; they fan to the left first. Then the second pair, called the swing pair, follow; then the third, the body pair; and finally the last, the wheel horses, the main pair that hold to make the turn. The horses must begin in order, with the wheel horses remaining still until the proper time; otherwise, the wagon could tip and fall over. The critical balance and synchronization of the eight horses and heavy wagon is considered at all times, with every second important in controlling the unit. If the body pair moves faster than the swing pair, the whole wagon could fall over or a horse could trip over the hitching. If the remaining horses continued to pull the wagon, a fallen horse could be seriously injured.

Perhaps the most exciting maneuver is the lead horses making a complete half circle to position the wagon at the curb. The lead horses come so close to the driver that, at times, he has handed the two horses each a piece of sugar from the palm of his hand.

The finale is the full gallop out of the ring. Ears erect and with a "tally ho!", the champion Clydesdales thunder away in a flamboyant departure.

The stableman harnesses each Clydesdale in a position in the hitch to allow the horses almost complete forward and backward movement. The skill and capability of the driver and his assistant determine the pace, position, and movement of each horse. While one man drives, the assistant driver straightens out the reins behind the driver's hands, insuring the driver complete control. The stress and tension of guiding the eighteen tons of horses and wagon is so great that the driver and assistant generally trade duties every fifteen to twenty minutes when the hitch is performing in long parades. If the main driver attempts to drive for more than fifteen to twenty minutes, he begins to lose feeling in his arms and fingers. It is imperative that the horses and driver stay in close contact at all times to assure the safety and perfection of the performance. If the driver's arms become numb or begin to hurt, his reactions would become too dull to react in time to the child that inevitably runs into the street to catch a closer glimpse of the approaching horses.

Anheuser-Busch owns two Clydesdale eight-horse hitches. Each travels around the country performing in state fairs, horse shows, and parades at company expense. One hitch travels the East Coast anywhere from Georgia to Louisiana, New York, Indiana, and back to St. Louis. The other covers the West Coast and Midwest, giving the public in such areas as California, Nebraska, Colorado, and Wyoming a chance to view the magnificent Clydesdales in person.

Following pages: left, *Clydesdales pulling St. Louis float in the Tournament of Roses Parade*; right, *Anheuser-Busch Clydesdale eight-horse hitch at Grant's Farm in St. Louis*

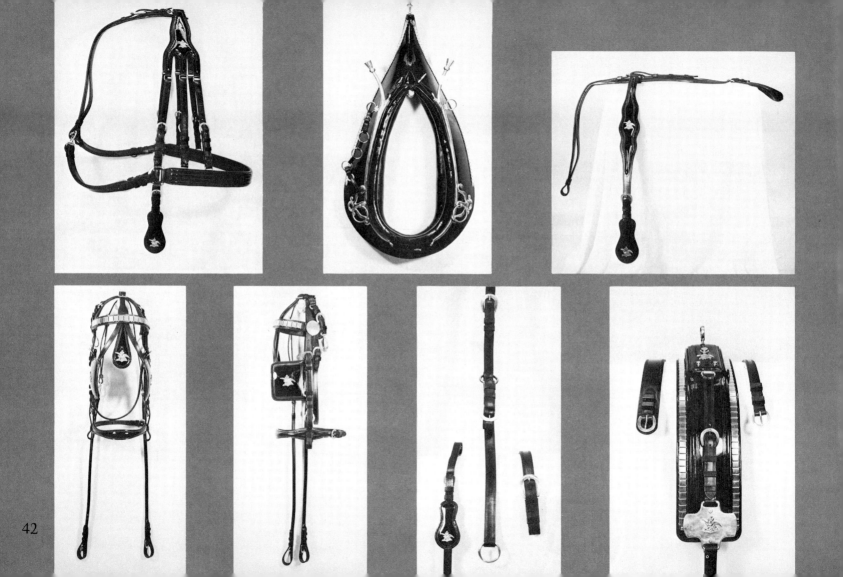

ANHEUSER-BUSCH HARNESSES

The lavishly decorated harnesses worn by the Anheuser-Busch Clydesdales are carefully handcrafted to Mr. Busch's exact specifications by Mr. John Santos of Great Barrington, Massachusetts. A talented and dedicated man, Mr. Santos always works alone to guarantee perfection of each harness. Only the finest materials are used—black leather imported from England and France, brass and silver for studs, and pure linen thread (seven pounds is used for a set of eight harnesses)—and he normally takes ten to twelve weeks to complete a set of eight harnesses.

The finished harness is a work of art, beautifully crafted and weighing over one hundred pounds. The single collar hung around the Clydesdale neck alone weighs seventy-five pounds. Mr. Santos's sensitivity to the Clydesdales is evident in every detail. He even twists their bits so they have something to play with during performances and parades!

Of course, these harnesses are expensive—each set of eight costs $28,000—but nothing is too good for the Clydesdales. They are harnesses fit for champions, and hours of polishing and washing and oiling by the stablemen keep them that way.

Left, Harness for hitch: above, left to right, *Breeching for wheel horses; Thirty-inch collar; Trace carriers for lead, swing, and body teams;* below, left to right, *Harness;*

Harness; Breast strap, pole strap, and martingale; Back pad with housing and girths
Above, Fully harnessed Clydesdale

43

CHAPTER 11

ANHEUSER-BUSCH CLYDESDALES' HISTORY

Today most of us know the Clydesdales as the symbol and roving good-will ambassadors of the Anheuser-Busch brewery. How this association developed is a story in itself.

For years, Anheuser-Busch in St. Louis used Clydesdales and other draft horses to pull their beer wagons, but no one thought then the mighty horses would become a universally known advertising symbol of the brewery. Oddly enough, it was during the Prohibition Era of 1920–1932 that the idea for the Clydesdales' future role was conceived.

During these years, August A. Busch, Jr., the son of the brewery's founder, was once watching a horse show given by the Wilson

Left, *Driver's view of eight-horse hitch*
Right, *Anheuser-Busch eight-horse hitch in New Hampshire snow*

Packing Company. As he chatted with employee Art Zerr (a fellow horse lover who later became one of the hitch drivers), a six-horse hitch of Clydesdales suddenly thundered into the brightly lit ring. Mr. Busch was amazed by the proud bearing and precise maneuvering of the horses and, at that moment, vowed that if and when prohibition were repealed, he would surprise his father with an eight-horse hitch of Clydesdales driven by Art Zerr.

Later, when Repeal seemed imminent, he kept the promise to himself and along with his brother Adolphus purchased twelve Clydesdales from the Wilson Packing Company and Chicago Stock Yard. Along with the horses, the "conspirators" bought harnesses, wagons, and all tack equipment available and secretly brought the lot to St. Louis to prepare and train for the big surprise.

On 7 April 1933, prohibition was repealed; the next day, August Busch's Clydesdales were ready. It was a beautiful stained-glass morning in

First case of "Bud" delivered to White House; left, August A. Busch, Sr.; center, Adolphus Busch, III; right, August A. Busch, Jr.

46

St. Louis. Mr. Busch, Sr., came down from his brewery office early, led to believe he was going to see son August's new car. Instead he was greeted by a stately review of an eight-horse team of Clydesdales pulling a brilliant red, white, and gold Anheuser-Busch beer wagon. Mr. Busch was stunned. His eyes welled with tears, and he could scarcely express his joyful gratitude at his son's commemoration of the brewery's past. The long drought was over and Budweiser Beer was back—in style!

As a gesture of thanks for the "Repeal," two of the first cases of "Bud" off the bottling line were delivered to Governor Al Smith of New York and President Roosevelt. In New York City, the Clydesdale hitch paraded down Fifth Avenue to meet Governor Smith at the Empire State Building; and in Washington, FDR received his case at the White House door after watching the team heather-step up the long driveway. It gave him as great a thrill as any procession of state.

ANHEUSER-BUSCH VANS

Today the Clydesdale eight-horse hitch and wagon design is officially registered as a trademark of Anheuser-Busch, Inc., and their stable in St. Louis is a national monument. There are two complete hitches, one for the East and one for the West; and each travels between 25,000 and 30,000 miles a year, at Anheuser-Busch expense, to perform in rodeos, horse shows, expositions, fairs, and parades such as the Tournament of Roses. Each hitch travels in a caravan of three forty- by eight-foot vans, two for the horses and one for the wagon, portable stalls, harnesses, tack equipment, medicine, and other necessities. A team of six men rides with each caravan: a driver, assistant driver,

Following pages, *World Famous Champion Anheuser-Busch Eight-Horse Hitch*

47

and four stablemen. The caravan always stops every few hundred miles so each horse can stretch his legs or have a little snack, such as a five-pound bag of carrots. At night when the caravan rests, one of the men stays with the horses to insure their comfort and safety.

The handsome dalmatians, "Barley" and "Hopps," are also a part of each entourage and are as much a brewery tradition as the Clydesdales themselves. Years ago, these dalmatians were bred and trained to protect the brewery horses. They would run alongside or underneath the wagon, barking to warn passersby to stay clear of the team. Today law requires the dogs to be seated, so "Barley" or "Hopps" now rides on the wagon seat next to the driver. Still, they are always in the spirit of things, and their enthusiastic barking is an ever-present part of each exciting performance.

Driver Walter Brady's life has been associated with horses since he was born in Greeley, Iowa, in 1919. As Greeley was the largest importer of Belgian draft horses in the United States, he became familiar with horses. At the age of fourteen, Walt started helping his father with his job at the Horse and Mule Association. During their free time, they gave hitching and horse-breaking demonstrations. After graduating from school, Walt began working for the Cudahy Meat Company, grooming and driving their draft horses. During World War II, he was in charge of shoeing 178 horses for the Army until they were replaced by cars, trucks, and jeeps. It was in the 1940s that Walt Brady began working for Anheuser-Busch. At this time, there are few others who have the remarkable talents and skills he has as a driver.

His assistant Del Tapsel was raised in Canada and surrounded by Clydesdales all his life. Del has been with Anheuser-Busch twenty years. The Walter Brady and Del Tapsel team is well known throughout the country.

Some of the drivers now retired and enjoying fond memories of their Clydesdale hitch driving years gone by are Billie Wales, who drove hitches at sixty years of age and received a silver trophy from the king and queen of England; Art Zerr, one of the first drivers after the Repeal of prohibition; and Harry Mueller, a fine gentleman known to most as "Whitey."

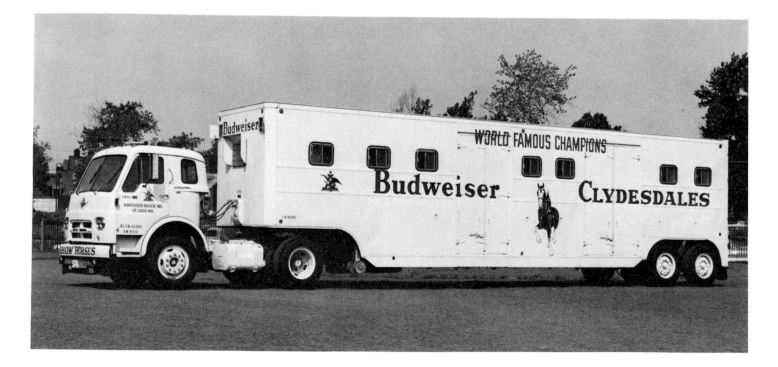

Traveling van for World Famous Champions

ANHEUSER-BUSCH STABLES

On the occasions when they are not traveling, the Clydesdales are resting at their home stable in St. Louis or at Busch Clydesdale Hamlet in Merrimack, New Hampshire.

The stable in St. Louis is especially fascinating and offers visitors not only a firsthand view of the horses, but also a glimpse into their colorful past. The building, part of the Anheuser-Busch brewery complex, is a fantasy of history and tradition. The entrance is through a pair of huge green sliding doors that open on a long hallway lined with trophies, mementos, and pictures of floats and parades of yesteryear. This corridor

Tack room at Anheuser-Busch St. Louis brewery

leads to the wagon room, where some of the first Anheuser-Busch wagons are exhibited along with a replica of the wagon pulled by the Clydesdales today. Dozens of vividly colored stained-glass windows surround the room, and an elegant chandelier from the 1904 World's Fair in St. Louis hangs from the ceiling.

The stable itself is reached by passing through a series of heavy wooden archways into an alcove. Here, in a spacious circular room, are the Clydesdale stalls—all gateless and decorated with elegant wrought-iron grills. The wooden floor of the stalls is generously covered with nineteen inches of straw to insure the horses' comfort.

The tack room, near the stalls, is no less ornate. It is quite narrow and lined with floor-to-ceiling mahogany and walnut armoires, each masterfully carved and with plate-glass front.

The whole luxurious setting certainly provides a fitting home for the gentle giants.

Armoires with harnesses at Anheuser-Busch St. Louis brewery

53

CONCLUSION

So these are the Clydesdales, the gentle giants—proud, poised, aristocrats of draft horses, heirs to the romantic tradition of great horses, legends in their own time, and beloved by all who know them. Each year they delight and stir the hearts of thousands with their flamboyant performances all over the country at rodeos, state fairs, and expositions—gates open and amid the roaring music of "The Ballad of The Big Ones" and rousing cheers, the eight-horse hitch charges with gusto into the floodlit arena—hooves pounding, dust flying, and dalmatian barking. Their brass and silver harness studs glitter like thousands of tiny gems in the bright floodlights, and with prancing heather step and drill-team precision, they perform their maneuvers to clamorous applause, parade around the ring, and gallop out in a thundering flourish. It is an unforgettable thrill.

These performances are the most conspicuous and spectacular display of the Clydesdale size, strength, and agility, and the resulting exposure has quickened national interest in the Clydesdale as both work horse and show horse. This appeal is not limited to North America; Scotland, England, South Africa, and Australia all have sizable Clydesdale populations.

There is a certain mystique, a certain magnetism, about the Clydesdales. Even laymen feel stirrings of mingled love, awe, and respect in their presence. Perhaps it is their imposing size, their physical beauty, their noble bearing, their agility, and responsiveness. Perhaps, since we are conditioned to think of most large animals as wild or unapproachable, we marvel at how such a powerful beast can be so patient and obliging. Or maybe it is the history, tradition, or even a wistful bit of lost Americana. But whatever the mystique, it is there. They are many things to many people, but one thing is certain, the gentle giants will continue to inspire and thrill young and old for generations to come.

Anheuser-Busch stables at St. Louis brewery

Following page, *The gentle giants at sunset*